CONGRATULATIONS!
You've Just Passed Grade 1

VIOLIN

GW00368108

<table>
	PIANO PART	VIOLIN PART
ANGELS	24	11
BASIN STREET BLUES	16	8
CAVATINA	26	12
DAISY BELL	9	4
A GROOVY KIND OF LOVE	2	1
HEIGH-HO	12	6
HOW DO I LIVE	22	10
I DON'T WANT TO MISS A THING	18	8
JEEPERS CREEPERS	4	2
MY HEART WILL GO ON (LOVE THEME FROM 'TITANIC')	6	3
SERENADE	10	5
SING A RAINBOW	20	9
THE WHITE CLIFFS OF DOVER	14	7
WE WISH YOU A MERRY CHRISTMAS	8	4
WHAT SHALL WE DO WITH THE DRUNKEN SAILOR	11	6
WHEN THE SAINTS GO MARCHING IN	3	2
</table>

Exclusive distributors:

International Music Publications Germany: Marstallstrasse 8, D-80539 München, Germany
Danmusik: Vognmagergade 7, DK-1120 Cioenhage K, Denmark
Nuova Carisch Srl.: Via Campania, 12, San Giuliano Milanese, Milano, Italy
Carisch France, SARL: 20, rue de la Ville-l'Eveque, 75008 Paris, France
Nueva Carisch Espana S.L.: Via Magallenes 25, 28015 Madrid, Spain

Production: Sadie Cook and Miranda Steel

Music arranged and processed by Barnes Music Engraving Ltd
East Sussex TN22 4HA, England

Cover design by xheight design limited

Published 1999

International Music Publications Limited
riffin House 161 Hammersmith Road London W6 8BS England

A Groovy Kind Of Love

Words and Music by Toni Wine and Carole Bayer-Sager

When The Saints Go Marching In

Traditional

Jeepers Creepers

Words by Johnny Mercer
Music by Harry Warren

My Heart Will Go On
(Love Theme from 'Titanic')

Words by Will Jennings
Music by James Horner

We Wish You A Merry Christmas

Traditional

Daisy Bell

Words and Music by Harry Dacre

Serenade

Joseph Haydn

What Shall We Do With The Drunken Sailor

Traditional

Heigh-Ho

Words by Larry Morey
Music by Frank E Churchill

The White Cliffs Of Dover

Words by Nat Burton
Music by Walter Kent

Basin Street Blues

Words and Music by Spencer Williams

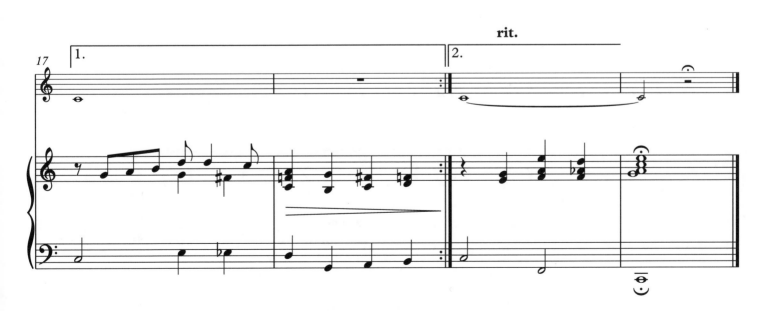

I Don't Want To Miss A Thing

Words and Music by Diane Warren

Slowly (♩ = 68)

© 1998 & 1999 Realsongs, USA
EMI Music Publishing Ltd, London WC2H 0EA

Sing A Rainbow

Words and Music by Arthur Hamilton

© 1955 & 1996 Mark VII Ltd
Warner/Chappell Music Ltd, London W6 8BS

How Do I Live

Words and Music by Diane Warren

Angels

Words and Music by Robbie Williams and Guy Chambers

Cavatina

Music by Stanley Myers

Printed by
Halstan & Co. Ltd., Amersham, Bucks., England

CONGRATULATIONS!

You've Just Passed Grade **1**

VIOLIN

A Groovy Kind Of Love

Words and Music by Toni Wine and Carole Bayer-Sager

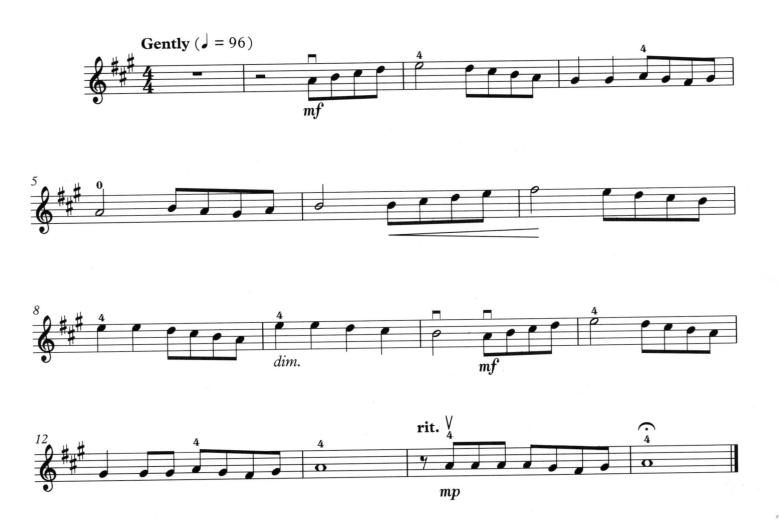

2

When The Saints Go Marching In

Traditional

Jeepers Creepers

Words by Johnny Mercer
Music by Harry Warren

My Heart Will Go On
(Love Theme from 'Titanic')

Words by Will Jennings
Music by James Horner

We Wish You A Merry Christmas

Traditional

Daisy Bell

Words and Music by Harry Dacre

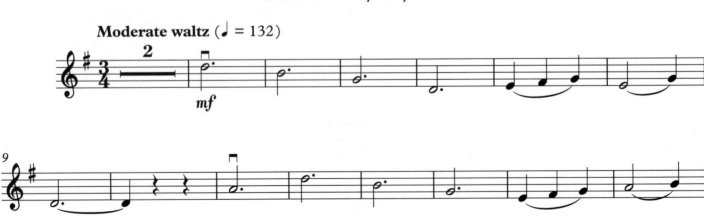

Serenade

Joseph Haydn

What Shall We Do With The Drunken Sailor

Traditional

Heigh-Ho

Words by Larry Morey
Music by Frank E Churchill

The White Cliffs Of Dover

Words by Nat Burton
Music by Walter Kent

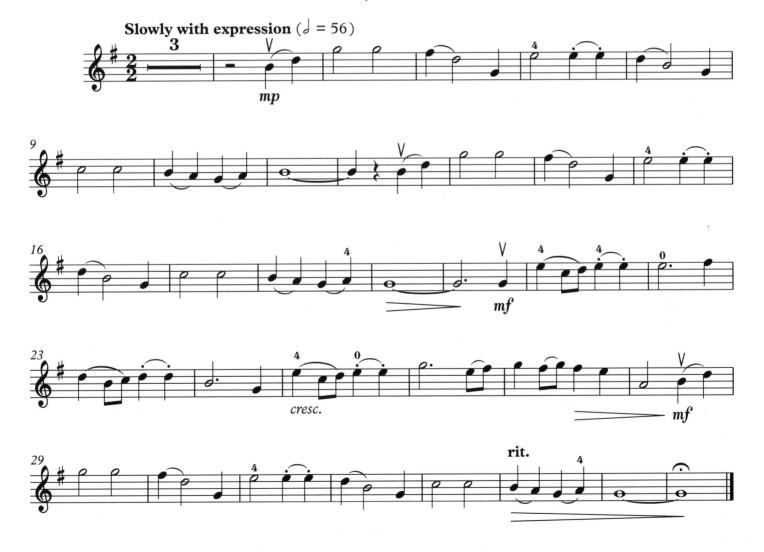

Basin Street Blues

Words and Music by Spencer Williams

I Don't Want To Miss A Thing

Words and Music by Diane Warren

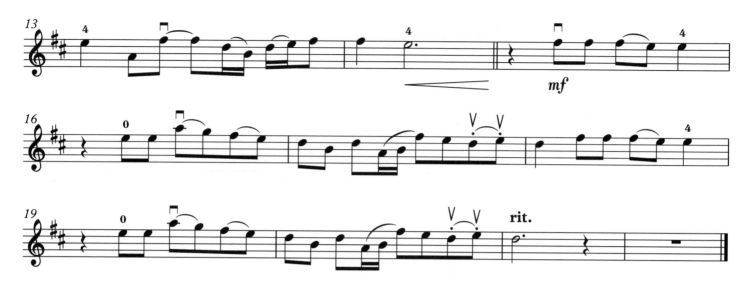

Sing A Rainbow

Words and Music by Arthur Hamilton

How Do I Live

Words and Music by Diane Warren

Angels

Words and Music by Robbie Williams and Guy Chambers

Cavatina

Music by Stanley Myers

Printed by
Halstan & Co. Ltd., Amersham, Bucks., England